The Perf 'Za

Jane Langford
Illustrated by Shelagh McNicholas

Mum was ill.
She was in bed.

Jack and his little sister Kate
wanted to make Mum feel better.
"Let's make Mum a pizza," said Jack.

"How do you make pizza?" asked Kate.

"It's easy," said Jack.

"You make a pizza base,
then you add toppings."

"What are toppings?" asked Kate.
"They are your favourite things to eat,"
said Jack, "like pepperoni or mushrooms.
You can ask Mum what toppings she likes."

Kate went upstairs to ask Mum,
but Mum was fast asleep.
"I'll ask Dad," thought Kate.

Kate went to see Dad.

Dad was in the study.

"Dad, what is Mum's favourite thing
to eat?" asked Kate.

"Chocolates," said Dad.

"I saw some in a box up there."

Dad gave the box of chocolates to Kate.

Kate went to see Grandma.

Grandma was in the garden.

"Grandma, what is Mum's favourite thing
to eat?" asked Kate.

"Marshmallows!" said Grandma.

"I have some in my pocket."

Grandma gave the marshmallows to Kate.

Then Mrs Price from next door
peeped over the fence.
"Are you having a picnic, Kate?"
asked Mrs Price.
"No," said Kate. "These are for Mum.
She's ill. She's in bed."
"Oh dear!" said Mrs Price.
"Here are some ginger biscuits for her.
Your mum loves ginger biscuits."

Kate went back to the kitchen.
She gave the chocolates, marshmallows,
and ginger biscuits to Jack.

"Chocolates, marshmallows, and ginger biscuits?
Are these Mum's favourite toppings?"
asked Jack.
"Yes!" said Kate.

Jack put the toppings on the pizza.
Then he put the pizza in the oven.

Soon, there was a wonderful smell.

Dad came into the kitchen.

Grandma came into the kitchen.

Mrs Price came into the kitchen.

Last of all, Mum came into the kitchen.

"What is that wonderful smell?" she asked.

"It's pizza," said Jack. "Try some."

"Mmmmm, chocolates," said Mum.
"Mmmmm, marshmallows.
Mmmmm, ginger biscuits!
My favourites!
Who chose the toppings?"

"THEY did!" said Kate.